The Encyclopedia of My Immaturity

Your Own Personal Diaryah

our attitude

KLUTZ®

creates activity books and other great stuff for kids ages 3 to 103. We began our corporate life in 1977 in a garage we shared with a Chevrolet Impala. Although we've outgrown that first office, Klutz Galactic Headquarters remains in Palo Alto, California, and we're still staffed entirely by real human beings. For those of you who collect mission statements, here's ours

Create wonderful things. Be good. Have fun.

Write us!

We would love to hear your comments regarding this or any of our books. We have many!

KLUTZ®
450 Lambert Avenue,
Palo Alto, CA 94306

our address

Visit our website!

You can check out all the stuff we make, find a nearby retailer, request a catalog, sign up for a newsletter, e-mail us or just goof off! www.klutz.com

Distributed in the UK by
Scholastic UK Ltd
Westfield Road
Southam, Warwickshire
England CV47 0RA

Distributed in Canada by
Scholastic Canada Ltd
604 King Street West
Toronto, Ontario
M5V 1E1
Canada

Distributed in Australia by
Scholastic Australia Ltd
PO Box 579
Gosford, NSW
Australia 2250

our lawyer

Book and pen manufactured in China. 73
ISBN 978-0-54534-971-0
4 1 5 8 5 7 0 8 8 8

DIARY?

Settle down. Deep breaths. This is not your average diary. We don't need to know your daily routine, or your lifelong dreams, or the name of that "certain someone who doesn't even know you exist." (Puh-leeze.) We want to document you and your immature life so far. That's it. So grab a pen and start filling in the pages. Celebrate yourself. It's time.

Diary Fakery: Parents... 6

Baby Sound & Smell... 8

About Grandpa... 10

About Grandma... 11

Foolish Quiz... 12

Stuff I Can Do... 14

Never Again... 15

Snap Decisions... 16

Deep Thought... 17

Diary Fakery: To Do List... 18

Cooking Report Cards... 20

Name Your Style... 22

Table of Contents

Your Lucky Underwear... 24

More Stuff I Can Do... 26

Never Again... 27

Snap Decisions... 28

Deep Thought... 29

Diary Fakery: Genius... 30

Air Guitar Hit List... 32

Lip Sync Hit List... 33

Your Rock Band... 34

Your Band T-Shirt... 35

Walks of Fame... 37

Noogies & Wet Willies... 38

Still More Stuff I Can Do... 40

Never Again... 41

Diary Fakery: Kindness... 42

Among Friends...44

Your Career Path... 46

Snap Decisions... 48

Deep Thought... 49

More Stuff I Can Do... 50

Never Again... 51

Self-Portraits... 52

Dear Me... 54

Diary Fakery!
On the next spread, fill in the blanks. Then leave the book open, so your snoopy parents will read it.

Dear Diary,

My Mom, _____ (your mom's name), must be the greatest mother in the history of mothers. And today she proved it again.

This morning I was being disagreeable. (probably due to the fact that I didn't get the good night's sleep Mom had suggested) I was Screaming, "_____" (made-up word) at my mom. "Leave me alone!!!" Thankfully, she didn't. She let me yell. Then she made a batch of her famous _____ (adjective) _____ (vegetable) cookies. They taste just like _____ (meat). Delicious. She then told me a story of when she was my age. It was just what I needed to hear. She really knows how a kid like me feels.

One Day, when I grow up, I promise to buy my mom _____ (number) _____ (adjective) _____ (plural noun). It's the least I can do to repay her.

MOTHER NAT

BEST MOM EV

← MOTHER GOOSE (DUH!)

6

Dear Diary,

My best friend, _best friend's name_ and I had an argument today. _best friend's name_ thinks _his/her_ dad is the coolest dad ever. Sure. ROTFL! There is no one cooler than, _dad's first name_ , a.k.a my dad

First of all, he can _verb_ faster than a _animal_ . Second, he can _verb_ higher than a _animal_ . Plus, he is stronger than a _animal_ and he can _verb_ like an angel. Some people don't believe this because my dad is so good looking. But trust me, it's 100 Percent FACT!!!

And he hasn't told me this yet, but I'm pretty sure he fights crime at night. That's right, I think my dad is the famous hero _made-up superhero_

So, my friend can think whatever they want, I know my dad is the greatest!

(7)

SOUND

Ask a parent to help answer these questions about your baby noises.

As an infant, I cried the loudest...

a when hungry   **b** when tired   **c** when hungry and tired   **d** whenever

When I cried it sounded like a...

a giggling dove   **b** sad kitty   **c** tiny firetruck   **d** chainsaw singing opera

The sound that always calmed me down and helped me fall asleep was...

a Mommy's voice   **b** Daddy's voice   **c** soft music   **d** Nothing. I didn't sleep. Ever!

The first word I spoke, that is NOT really a word, was...

a goo goo   **b** ga ga   **c** mooshie-moo   **d** phhhrt   **e** other _____

The first word I spoke, that IS a real word, was...

a Mama   **b** Dada   **c** baby   **d** ball   **e** other _____

The word that I used to love to yell (that drove my parents nuts)

a Mine!   **b** Noooooo!   **c** Pooopie!   **d** Stupid!   **e** other _____

&SMELL

Ask a parent to help answer these questions about your diaper days.

When my diaper was full, I would let my parents know by...
- **a** crying
- **b** pointing at it
- **c** winking at them
- **d** sending an e-mail

My mother tells me that my dirty diapers smelled like...
- **a** roses
- **b** fresh cut grass
- **c** a bouquet of tuips
- **d** She'd rather not say.

My father tells me that my dirty diapers smelled like...
- **a** toxic sludge
- **b** toxic mud
- **c** toxic funk
- **d** toxic pudding with toxic toppings

The typical color of my used diapers was...
- **a** brown-ish
- **b** yellow-ish
- **c** green-ish
- **d** other: _____-ish

The most difficult diaper change my parents completed was...
- **a** trunk of a car
- **b** in a shopping cart
- **c** on an airplne, during a turbulent flight
- **d** other (please describe, in gross detail) _____
  _____
  _____

9

Your grandfather is always calm and collected. As mature as they come, right? Don't believe it. Ask your grandfather what he did for fun as a kid. What made his friends laugh?

_____

_____

_____

_____

_____

_____

_____

_____

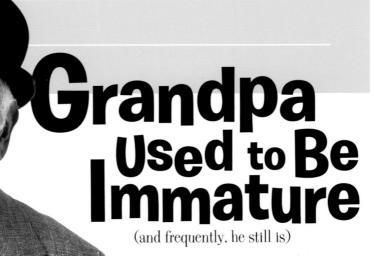

Grandpa
Used to Be
Immature
(and frequently, he still is)

Your grandma is so gentle and sweet. Could she have been a troublemaker when she was young? You bet. Ask your grandma what she did for fun as a kid. What made her friends laugh?

_____

_____

_____

_____

_____

_____

_____

Grandma
Used to Be
Immature
(and occasionally, she still is)

1. In the morning when the alarm clock goes off I always...

    (a) leap out of bed, singing at the top of my lungs

    (b) hit the snooze alarm, grumbling under my breath

    (c) What alarm clock? I didn't hear anything?

2. For breakfast I always eat a nutritious breakfast that includes...

    (a) using bacon as drumsticks on my sister's head

    (b) reading the cereal box ingredients panel out loud

    (c) a spoon of white sugar on my bowl full of colorful sugar

3. At school my favorite time of the day is...

    (a) saying good morning to all my adoring fans and teachers

    (b) science, math, and computers

    (c) I don't understand this question.

4. At school my least favorite time of the day is...

    (a) quiet time. What's the point?

    (b) P.E. What's the point?

    (c) the "school" part. What's the point?

5. On the weekends I love to spend time...

    (a) goofing around with my crazy friends

    (b) playing video games online with my friends

    (c) reading Shakespeare. OK, I'm kidding. Napping.

6. The most frequent thing my parents tell me is...

    (a) You're too old for the bouncy house.

    (b) Put down that book and get some sun.

    (c) You're late! Didn't you hear the alarm clock?

7. The most frequent thing I say back to my parents is...

    (a) No one is too old for the bouncy house!

    (b) This book is all about solar flares. So I'm getting lots of sun.

    (c) What alarm clock? I didn't hear anything?

What Kind of Fool Am I?

First: Take the quiz at left. Circle the answers that best fit you.

Second: Add up your score. Each **a** 1 point, **b** 2 points, **c** 3 points.

Find out what kind of fool you are.

7-11 POINTS
Life of the Party

12-16 POINTS
King of the Sci-Fi Convention

17-21 POINTS
Lord of the Nap

"I can belch the alphabet up to the letter _____."
(on a single belch, of course)

"I once scored _____ points on a pinball machine."

Minor Achievements = Major Pride

I AM AWE-SOME

"I once flicked _____ cherries into my mouth off the back of my hand. Before I missed."

"I have washed the dishes without being asked."   yes   no

"During my life, I have broken _____ bones in my body."

"I once hit my principal with a water balloon."

Accidentally, of course.

But still...

NEVER AGAIN!

Describe something that you did once, but probably won't do again.

_____

_____

_____

_____

_____

Snap Decisions

Sometimes the choices are easy. Circle your favorite.

snowboarding	or	skiing
football	or	basketball
dogs	or	cats
grizzly bears	or	koala bears
funny movies	or	scary movies
spiders	or	snakes
chocolate	or	vanilla
right-handed	or	left-handed
tomato	or	to-mah-to

Pick me!

Pick me!

DeepThought

Which super power is best: mind-reading, seeing the future, or the ability to stop time? Why?

_____

_____

_____

_____

_____

_____

_____

_____

_____

Use your best "Deep Thought" Face

Diary Fakery!
On the next spread, fill in the blanks. Then leave the book open, so your snoopy parents will read it.

DAILY TO DO LIST FOR your name

☐ WAKE UP EARLY, IN A GREAT MOOD!
☐ Make my bed immediately
☐ Get dressed. TUCK SHIRT,
☐ Brush teeth, floss, wash face. Towel off bathroom sink and wipe clean all toothpaste splatter from the mirror
☐ Comb hair neatly. AWAY from face.
☐ walk with a bounce in my step to the breakfast table. (try skipping. Fun!)

☐ Make a hearty, nutritious, balanced breakfast. EAT fruit, It's good for you.
☐ make small talk with your family try "How Bout this weather, huh?"

☐ Clear your dishes, skip off to school.

More daily TO DO LIST FOR your name

- ☐ Smile and say good morning to fellow students at school. No grunting.
- ☐ Sit up straight in desk. No slouching.
- ☐ pay attention
- ☐ Stare out the window and day dream
- ☐ PAY ATTENTION??
- ☐ After school, walk home, stopping only to smell flowers and/or to help old people cross the street.

- ☐ At home, do homework immediately.
- ☐ Evening, set the table for dinner, ask Mom and Dad about their day. Help clear the table after dinner. Skip television.

- ☐ Get to bed at 9pm. 9:30 at the latest

BREAKFAST

Name of Dish: _____

Ingredients: _____

_____

Color:	Dazzling	Neat	Boring	Ugly
Smell:	Thrilling	Decent	Zero	Hideous
Texture:	Creamy	Crunchy	Chewy	Scary
Flavor:	Yummy	Yawn	Yuck	Yak

A GREAT WAY TO START THE DAY? Yep! ☐ Nope! ☐

draw the reality

MOM'S *Cooking*

SANDWICH

see perfection

Name of Sandwich: _____

Ingredients: _____

_____

Color:	Dazzling	Neat	Boring	Ugly
Smell:	Thrilling	Decent	Zero	Hideous
Texture:	Creamy	Crunchy	Chewy	Scary
Flavor:	Yummy	Yawn	Yuck	Yak

A GREAT MIDDAY MEAL? Yep! ☐ Nope! ☐

draw the reality

DINNER

Name of Dish: _____

Ingredients: _____

_____

see perfection

Color:	Dazzling	Neat	Boring	Ugly
Smell:	Thrilling	Decent	Zero	Hideous
Texture:	Creamy	Crunchy	Chewy	Scary
Flavor:	Yummy	Yawn	Yuck	Yak

LOOK FORWARD TO EATING THIS AGAIN? Yep! ☐ Nope! ☐

draw the reality

REPORT CARDS

DESSERT

Name of Dish: _____

Ingredients: _____

_____

see perfection

Color:	Dazzling	Neat	Boring	Ugly
Smell:	Thrilling	Decent	Zero	Hideous
Texture:	Creamy	Crunchy	Chewy	Scary
Flavor:	Yummy	Yawn	Yuck	Yak

LIP-SMACKING, FINGER-LICKING GOOD? Yep! ☐ Nope! ☐

draw the reality

Name your Style

Look at all the words around the **white figure** → Without thinking too much, circle the first five that remind you of you. That's your style.

Over-the-top
Fierce Cowboy
Nordic
Bat-like
Wicked Cool
Spiffy
Spaced-out Preppie
Skinky Tidy
Sad Retro
Edgy
Lived-in
Down-home
Hip-hugger
Wrinkle-Free
Totally cool
Wrinkle-Rich
Laid-back
Cheesy
Different
Phat
Slick
Cringe-making
Back-to-the-Future
Nerdy
Accidental
Twisted
Superstar
No-fuss
Chocolate-smeared
Neat
Whatever
Hot
Biker Notorious
Nifty
Everyday
Fuzzy
Dapper
Lopsided
Button-downer
Pizza-Chic
Dorky Grass-stained

My look is called

_____

_____

_____

_____

_____

Ask for it by name.

HOW TO FIND

Document your underwear for a week.

MONDAY

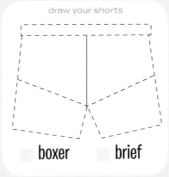

draw your shorts

☐ boxer   ☐ brief

Color: _____

Pattern: _____

Good things that happened:

_____

_____

Bad things that happened:

_____

_____

_____

☐ Lucky, wear everyday!
☐ Unlucky, throw away.
☐ Just underwear

TUESDAY

draw your shorts

☐ boxer   ☐ brief

Color: _____

Pattern: _____

Good things that happened:

_____

_____

Bad things that happened:

_____

_____

_____

☐ Lucky, wear everyday!
☐ Unlucky, throw away.
☐ Just underwear

WEDNESDAY

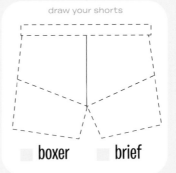

draw your shorts

☐ boxer   ☐ brief

Color: _____

Pattern: _____

Good things that happened:

_____

_____

Bad things that happened:

_____

_____

_____

☐ Lucky, wear everyday!
☐ Unlucky, throw away.
☐ Just underwear

YOUR *Lucky* UNDERWEAR

Determine which pair lead to good things happening, and which don't.

THURSDAY

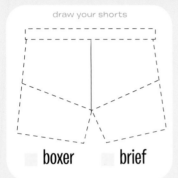

draw your shorts

☐ boxer   ☐ brief

Color: _____

Pattern: _____

Good things that happened:

_____

_____

_____

Bad things that happened:

_____

_____

_____

☐ Lucky, wear everyday!
☐ Unlucky, throw away.
☐ Just underwear

FRIDAY

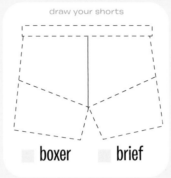

draw your shorts

☐ boxer   ☐ brief

Color: _____

Pattern: _____

Good things that happened:

_____

_____

_____

Bad things that happened:

_____

_____

_____

☐ Lucky, wear everyday!
☐ Unlucky, throw away.
☐ Just underwear

WEEKEND

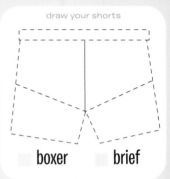

draw your shorts

☐ boxer   ☐ brief

Color: _____

Pattern: _____

Good things that happened:

_____

_____

_____

Bad things that happened:

_____

_____

_____

☐ Lucky, wear everyday!
☐ Unlucky, throw away.
☐ Just underwear

"I know ⬭ ways to say the word dude."

"I've gone to school with mismatched socks ⬭ times."

"I can spin a basketball on my finger for ⬭ seconds."

"My longest weekend nap was ⬭ hours."

"I once ate ⬭ slices of pizza in a row."

NEVER AGAIN!

Describe something that you did once, but probably won't do again.

_____

_____

_____

_____

_____

Snap Decisions

Sometimes the choices are easy. Circle your favorite.

drum solos	or	guitar solos
kickball	or	dodgeball
roller blades	or	skateboard
with cheese	or	without cheese
the tortoise	or	the hare
checkers	or	chess
Bert	or	Ernie
circling	or	underlining
plain	or	peanut

Pick me!

Pick me!

Deep Thought

What are five reasons it's great to be a kid?

_____

_____

_____

_____

_____

_____

_____

Use your best "Deep Thought" Face

Diary Fakery!
On the next spread, draw a graph. Then leave the book open, so your snoopy parents will read it.

TOO EASY!! BO-RING! "2+2=4" dull?

Homework Warm-up Exercises

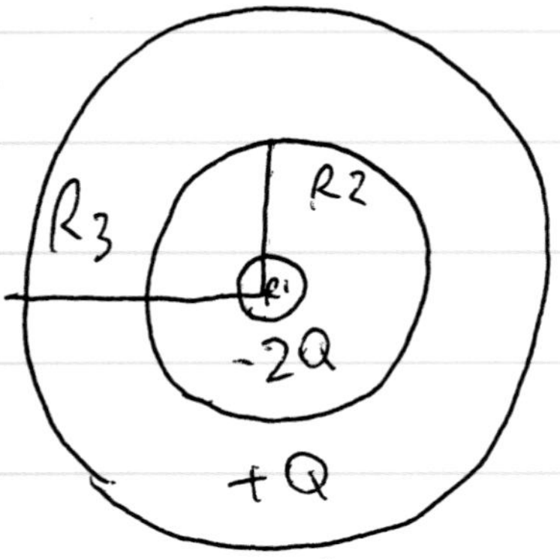

+3 б

Inside of $R_1 = 0$

Since inside of R_1 is "isolated"

Outside of R_1 must be -2Q to get total change on small shell to cancel out -2Q change from outside of R_1 inside of R_2 must be +2Q

To get total of +Q on R_2 outside of R_2 must be -Q. Thus, inside of R_3 Must cancel out -Q so it is equal to +Q! TOO EASY

Inside of R_3 = +Q

$\varepsilon_0 \oint E\, dA$ q inc

draw a graph here, it doesn't need to make any sense.

① letty y = 0   0 ≤ x ≥ 2

dA = $-\hat{j}$ Ɛ.5(3.0î + 2.5

② Ɛ..25(-1) Sda)

C'mon! Too OBVIOUS!

①&② cancel out (symmetry)

Total change contained in the cube

How To Turn Your Toilet INTO a NUClear Power Plant!

URANIUM (Use Gloves!)

TURBINE

COMPRESSOR

COOLING

RODS OF FUEL

TREADMILL

↳ WHY IT WILL WORK ⟩

$$2\hbar \frac{dx}{dt} = Hx$$

$$2\hbar \begin{pmatrix} \dot{a} \\ \dot{b} \end{pmatrix} = \frac{g\rho}{2} \left(NN \begin{pmatrix} B_2 & B_x \cos wt \\ B_x \cos wt & -B_2 \end{pmatrix} \begin{pmatrix} a \\ b \end{pmatrix} \right.$$

$$\begin{pmatrix} \dot{a} \\ \dot{b} \end{pmatrix} = -2' \frac{g_\rho NN}{2\hbar} \begin{pmatrix} B_2 & B_x \cos wt \\ B_x \cos wt & -B_2 \end{pmatrix} \begin{pmatrix} a \\ b \end{pmatrix}$$

$$= -2' \begin{pmatrix} w_1 \begin{smallmatrix} w_0 \\ \cos wt \end{smallmatrix} & w_1 \cos wt \\ & -w_0 \end{pmatrix} \begin{pmatrix} a \\ b \\ a \\ b \end{pmatrix}$$

HIT LIST
Air Guitar

I shred the air on these six songs.

1 Title: _____
Artist: --------------------

2 Title: _____
Artist: --------------------

3 Title: _____
Artist: --------------------

4 Title: _____
Artist: --------------------

5 Title: _____
Artist: --------------------

6 Title: _____
Artist: --------------------

HIT LIST
Lip-Syncing

I fake-rock the mic to these songs.

1 Title: _____
Artist: _____

2 Title: _____
Artist: _____

3 Title: _____
Artist: _____

4 Title: _____
Artist: _____

5 Title: _____
Artist: _____

6 Title: _____
Artist: _____

How can you stay immature forever but still look cool?

Start Your Own Rock Band

The first thing any band needs is a **good name**. Here's how you do it. Fill in the blanks in box **B**. Then just pick one name from box **A** and combine it with one name from box **B**. (Two names from **A** also works well.)

A

AGENT

THE INEVITABLE

WHISPERING

FLESH-EATING

FLAME-DRINKING

DISASTER

HAUNTED

GELATINOUS

TENDER

MOTHER

LONG DISTANCE

B

_____
YOUR MIDDLE NAME

_____
LAST NAME OF YOUR FAVORITE TEACHER

_____
A COLOR YOU LIKE BUT DON'T LOVE

_____
ANY WORD THAT BEGINS WITH "H"

_____
FLAVOR OF ICE CREAM

_____
CUDDLY ANIMALS

_____
BODY PART

_____
HEAVY OBJECT

_____
LAST TWO DIGITS OF YOUR PHONE NUMBER

_____
CARTOON CHARACTER

_____
YOUR ZODIAC SIGN

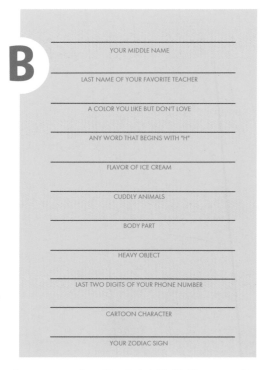

"Ladies and Gentlemen welcome to the stage, the Rock 'n' Roll Power of

"

_____
WRITE YOUR NEW BAND NAME

YOUR BAND's TOUR T-SHIRT
FRONT
Draw your new band's logo? Or the name of your new record. Or just a big shape? Your fans will buy anything.

YOUR BAND's TOUR T-SHIRT
BACK

List the places your band will play on the tour. Countries, cities, or just other friends' houses.

THE SNEAK
☐ CAN DO

THE EGYPTIAN
☐ CAN DO

THE CRAB WALK
☐ CAN DO

Walks of Fame
To be truly immature, you must know how to walk. Please prove you can do these famous walks.

THE HIGH STEP
☐ CAN DO

THE ZOMBIE
☐ CAN DO

Sometimes people annoy you. How to keep track?

Make a list and assign the approprate, immature response.

NOOGIE,

The noogie zone

To poke or rub another's head with knuckles.

WET WILLIE,

A freshly licked finger, stuck into another's ear.

or FLAT TIRE?

To step on the back of another's shoe and make it fall off.

Like this.
Classic.

Name of annoyer	Annoying offense	Noogie	Wet Willie	Flat Tire
				39

"I can juggle 3 tennis balls for ⬭ minutes."

"I can impersonate the sound of a helicopter and a machine gun."
⬤ yes ⬤ no

I AM AWE-SOME

"I can curl my tongue into the shape of a taco.
⬤ yes ⬤ no

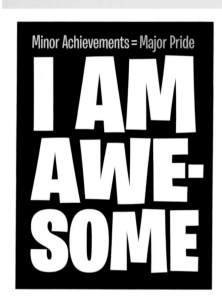

"Using only my sense of smell, I can find my shoes with my eyes closed."
⬤ yes ⬤ no

"I can stand on my head for ⬭ minutes."

"I once tried this really cool trick where I put a plunger on my head..."

NEVER AGAIN!

Describe something that you did once, but probably won't do again.

_____

_____

_____

_____

_____

_____

_____

Diary Fakery!

On the next spread, fill in the blanks. Then leave the book open, so your snoopy parents will read it.

Dear Diary

Me again, I found a dollar today. And I'm having a difficult time deciding which charity to give it to.

My mom will probably want me to give it to Association of _____ plural noun

They're a good organization. But my Dad will say I should give the dollar to his favorite charity. They also do good work. And with every donation they send back a T-Shirt with a _____ animal on it. I dunno. It's a tough choice.

My Friend _____ friend's name says I should just spend the dollar on that new candy bar, The _____ adjective _____ sea animal _____ flavor Bar.

But that's just not the type of person I am. Whenever I have any money I save it or I share it with someone in need.

VEGETABLE GROWING RESEARCH $1 DOLLAR$

THE DAD CHARITY

Dear Diary,

I know that I fight a lot with my __brother/sister__, it's kind of normal to fight with your siblings. But just between you and me, Diary, I really love my __brother/sister__. They're really cool.

There was one time when I put their __favorite thing__ in the bathtub. AAAAAUGH!!! And the time I hid their __piece of clothing__ in the trunk of the car. And, of course the, the famous incident, when I told Mom that they had __verb (past tense)__ on the principal at school. I lied. And it was funny. But now I know they didn't deserve it. My bad.

I hereby promise to stop bothering my __brother/sister__. And when they bother me I will be understanding. After all, that is what family is all about.

(43)

your first best friend

First name: _____

Middle name: _____

Nickname: _____

Birthday: _____

Allergies: _____

Is really good at playing:

1. _____

2. _____

Is not so good at playing:

1. _____

2. _____

Secretly afraid of:

_____

Be a Good Best Friend

Fill in these friendly cheat sheets to be a better friend.

Easy.

your second best friend

First name: _____

Middle name: _____

Nickname: _____

Birthday: _____

Allergies: _____

Is really good at playing:

1. _____

2. _____

Is not so good at playing:

1. _____

2. _____

Secretly afraid of:

_____

your third best friend

First name: _____

Middle name: _____

Nickname: _____

Birthday: _____

Allergies: _____

Is really good at playing:

1. _____

2. _____

Is not so good at playing:

1. _____

2. _____

Secretly afraid of:

_____

your fourth best friend

First name: _____

Middle name: _____

Nickname: _____

Birthday: _____

Allergies: _____

Is really good at playing:

1. _____

2. _____

Is not so good at playing:

1. _____

2. _____

Secretly afraid of:

_____

your fifth best friend

First name: _____

Middle name: _____

Nickname: _____

Birthday: _____

Allergies: _____

Is really good at playing:

1. _____

2. _____

Is not so good at playing:

1. _____

2. _____

Secretly afraid of:

_____

BEST FRIEND CONTRACT

I _____ , being of immature mind and body, hereby profess my eternal friend-i-tude to my best bud, _____ . We are solid, we are unbreakable, we are one. And we promise to..

[choose three]

- cheer each other's teams
- develop a secret handshake
- split the last donut in the box
- save each other a seat at the movies
- let each other ride on the handlebars
- make a fort and exclude younger siblings
- have each other's backs (whatever that means)

- split every bag of chips
- high five too much
- sing loudly in the back seat
- burp in harmony
- not comment on each other's haircuts
- watch the same TV shows
- listen to the same music

And here are our signatures to prove it!

Date _____

We're in this together!

What will you Barely grow up to be?

Science & Math

Math mostly...
- counting money
- counting my fingers

Science mostly...
- explosions
- eating weird things then trying to guess what they were after I eat them.
- watching the changing colors of cheese melting on hot pavement.

You Are Here
See where your interests lead you.

Language & The Arts

The Arts mostly...
- painting & drawing
- poetry

Language mostly...
- talking about myself

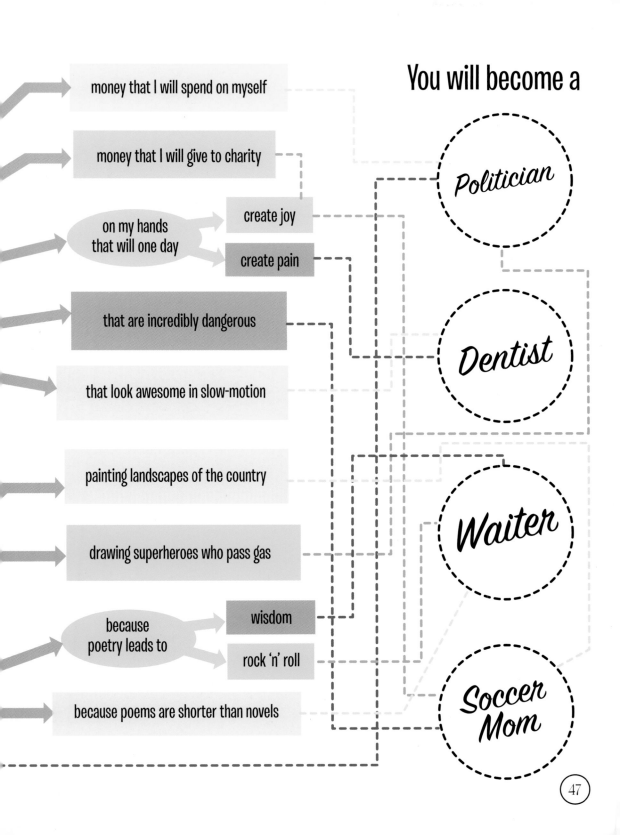

You will become a

money that I will spend on myself

money that I will give to charity

on my hands that will one day

create joy

create pain

that are incredibly dangerous

that look awesome in slow-motion

painting landscapes of the country

drawing superheroes who pass gas

because poetry leads to

wisdom

rock 'n' roll

because poems are shorter than novels

Politician

Dentist

Waiter

Soccer Mom

Snap Decisions

Sometimes the choices are easy. Circle your favorite.

television	or	movies
root beer	or	lemonade
the beach	or	the mountains
hot dog	or	hamburger
knight	or	ninja
ice cream	or	cake
the park	or	the mall
trains	or	planes
truth	or	dare

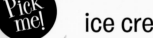
Pick me!

Pick me!

Deep Thought

When you become a parent, what will you do differently from your parents? What will you do the same? Hmm?

_____

_____

_____

_____

_____

_____

_____

_____

_____

Use your best "Deep Thought" Face

"I once played video games for _____ straight hours."

"I have taken out the trash **without** having been asked."
● yes ● no

Minor Achievements = Major Pride

I AM AWE-SOME

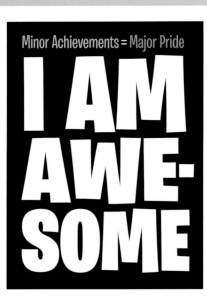

"I can whistle through my fingers."
● yes
● no

"I have combed my hair _____ times in the past week."

"I know how to tuck in my shirt"
● yes ● no

"I once ate 5 pounds of candy corn!"

NEVER AGAIN!

Describe something that you did once, but probably won't do again.

_____

_____

_____

_____

_____

Self-Portrait

PRESENT

Draw
yourself
as you look,
right now.

Self-Portrait FUTURE

Draw
yourself
as you will
look 10 years
from right now.

Dear "Mature" Me,

Use this page to write your future self a letter about what it was like to be immature. Then remove it and seal it in an envelope. Store the envelope, and read it in 10 years.

Thanks

The folks who made this diary possible

Leader of The Goofballs:
Michael Sherman

Immature Role Model:
John Cassidy

Fountain of Youth:
Eva Steele-Saccio

Photographic Tom-Foolery:
Peter Fox

Diary Fakery Illustration:
Jaime Martinez

Queen of the Foil:
Patty Morris

Man-aging Editor:
Gary Mcdonald

Editorial Assistants:
Susan DeLance
Rebekah Lovato

Contributions:
Ben Grossblatt
Brian McMullen
Bryan Okamoto
Michael Sherman
Valerie Wyatt

Photo credits:
Page 8 sunemotion/IStockphotos.
Page 20 MentalArt/IStockphoto.
Page 21 Joe Gough/Shutterstock.
Page 34 m-i-s-h-a-/Istockphoto.
Page 44 Eric Isselee

Looking For More?

Here are some simple ways to keep the Klutz coming:

1 Get your hands on a copy of the Klutz Catalog. To request a free copy of our mail order catalog, go to klutz.com/catalog.

2 Become a Klutz Insider and get e-mail about new releases, special offers, contests, games, goofiness, and who-knows-what-all. If you're a grown-up who wants to receive e-mail from Klutz, head to klutz.com/insider

If any of this sounds good to you, but you don't feel like going online right now, just give us a call at 1-800-737-4123.

More Great Books From Klutz

The Encyclopedia of Immaturity Vol. 1
The Encyclopedia of Immaturity Vol. 2

The Klutz Book of Inventions
The Klutz Book of Paper Airplanes
Invasion of the Bristlebots
Quick Draw Flip Books

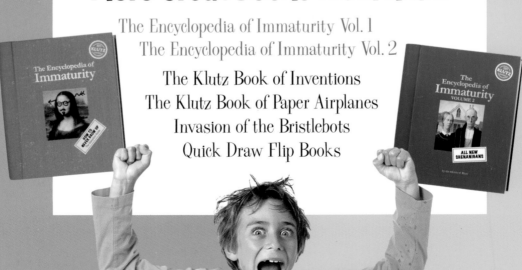